I-SPY

Ol
MOTORWAY
· & CAR NUMBERS ·

This book belongs to:

Chris Wright

Before you join a motorway, there will be a signpost to show where it is. A sign with a blue background on another main road indicates that the motorway begins from the junction ahead. Look out for yellow squares, triangles, diamonds, and circles, too. These mark emergency diversions for motorway traffic, so the driver follows circles, or squares, and so on.
I-Spy for 5

A sign with a green background is a primary route whereas local direction signs are white with black letters and a blue border.
I-Spy for 5

You will see this kind of motorway designation sign at a junction which leads directly to the motorway itself.
I-Spy for 5

This shows the start of the motorway and the point where the driver must follow the motorway regulations. Older signs had a list of the motorway rules but these are being phased out.
I-Spy for 5

Motorways may have different numbers of lanes on each carriageway, usually depending upon how much traffic the planners expected the motorway to carry:

...three lanes
I-Spy for 5

...four lanes
I-Spy for 10

...or even five lanes
I-Spy for 15

Sometimes, if a motorway has to be built on the side of a hill, the carriageways may be at different levels.
I-Spy for 20

MERGING MOTORWAYS

Here, as indicated by the junction number 3a, a new junction has been made on the motorway between the existing junctions 3 and 4. Traffic wishing to follow the M42 leading to the M1 and M6, and so on should stay in the left-hand lane.
I-Spy for 15

As more and more new motorways are built, continuous routes are constructed by linking one motorway with another. This sign indicates that, in 1/3 mile, two motorways merge.
I-Spy for 15

On the main two lanes of a motorway, this sign indicates that two motorways are merging with one lane joining from the left.
I-Spy for 15

And here there are two motorway lanes merging into one and then joining from the left.
I-Spy for 15

Look out for these road markings where motorways merge.
I-Spy for 15

A triangular sign with a red border is a warning sign. This temporary sign warns of roadworks on the motorway in 3 miles time. Notice that it has been weighed down with sandbags to stop it blowing over.
I-Spy for 15

This is another temporary warning sign that speaks for itself. But notice that, at night, it can be illuminated by a gas-burning lamp.
I-Spy for 15

If you see this sign in December, it doesn't mean that you'll be stuck in a traffic jam for seven months! It does mean that they expect that the roadworks 1 mile ahead will continue until July.
I-Spy for 15

ROADWORKS

This is a special sign for traffic carrying loads wider than 9 feet 6 inches wide. It means that the lanes are narrow and that the load must be accompanied by a police escort.
I-Spy for 20

On a three-lane motorway where there are roadworks in ³/₄ mile, this sign shows that the right-hand lane is blocked and indicates which lane the traffic should follow for particular routes. You will see this where the roadworks includes a junction area.
I-Spy for 20

A sign like this one indicates that, in 200 yards, the outside lane is closed and that traffic should move to the left.
I-Spy for 20

This one is more specific and indicates that the inside lane of the two remaining lanes should be the emergency hard shoulder.
I-Spy for 20

Sometimes the whole carriageway of a motorway is under repair so that the traffic flows in opposite lanes divided by temporary markers on the remaining carriageway. This is called a 'contraflow'.
I-Spy for 20

This sign indicates the end of a contraflow so that traffic can return to the normal carriageways.
I-Spy for 20

And finally the end of the roadworks on this part of the motorway.
I-Spy for 15

7

MATRIX SIGNALS

Look out for the overhead gantries which carry matrix signals that can be lit up when necessary. In this case, they are unlit.
I-Spy for 5

This overhead matrix signal is illuminated and indicates a temporary maximum speed of 50 mph in the left-hand lane and tells traffic in the right-hand lane to change lanes to the left.
I-Spy for 20

And this one signals to change lanes to the right where there is a 50 mph speed limit.
I-Spy for 20

This one instructs that the temporary maximum speed limit for all lanes is 50 mph.
I-Spy for 15

These overhead signals indicate a maximum temporary speed of 30 mph on both lanes of the motorway.
I-Spy for 20

There are five lanes of traffic here. Notice the illuminated overhead matrix signals. The two right-hand lanes have a temporary speed limit of 60 mph. But the illuminated red crosses with flashing red lights instruct traffic not to proceed any further in those lanes. In effect, this is a motorway closure here.
I-Spy for 25

This is an old-version matrix signal indicating the end of any temporary restrictions when it is illuminated.
I-Spy for 25

MATRIX SIGNALS

This roadside signal with its flashing yellow lights and illuminated 50 indicates a temporary maximum speed of 50 mph perhaps because of bad driving conditions such as fog.
I-Spy for 15

Here is a roadside signal indicating that the right-hand lane is closed ahead. On a busy road, these illuminated signs are 1 mile apart, and they are 2 miles apart on a rural road.
I-Spy for 15

Modern illuminated signs indicating the end of a temporary restriction just say 'End'.
I-Spy for 15

Where there are no matrix signals, a temporary speed limit of 50 mph might be indicated by a sign like this one. A round signal with a red border gives an order. This one can be lit up at night by a gas lamp.
I-Spy for 15

This is called a 'Vibraline'. On a motorway, it is used to mark the boundary between the inside lane and the emergency hard shoulder. If a driver accidentally strays on to the hard shoulder, the raised parts of the line make the tyres vibrate noisily to remind the driver to correct his/her line.
I-Spy for **15**

When a 'contraflow' is operating on a motorway, it is the responsibility of the Local Authority to erect temporary lighting over that stretch of road. (A 'contraflow' is a length of motorway in which traffic has been diverted from one carriageway to the other so that it is travelling in the opposite direction from normal.)
I-Spy for **15**

Here's an unusual one — a cattle grid on a motorway. Cattle grids are rather like wide ditches with an iron grid across the top so that the traffic can pass over but, if a farm animal tried, its foot would go down between the bars of the grid. Animals soon learn this and do not try to cross the grid.
I-Spy for **50**

These marker posts are positioned at 100-metre intervals along the motorway. They are numbered and arrowed to indicate where the nearest emergency telephone is. This means that if you have to use the phone, you can tell the police exactly where you are by announcing the number on the post.
I-Spy for 5

You will see these emergency phones all along the motorway. There is no charge for using the phone if you are in difficulty and you connect straight through to the local police force.
I-Spy for 5

...and inside the phone box.
I-Spy for 15

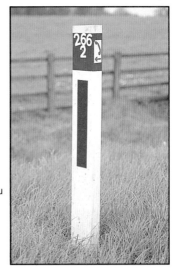

Here is an unusual I-Spy. The editor admits that he doesn't know exactly what it is.
I-Spy for 25
Double if you can find out what it is

All over the country, transmission towers (they are sometimes incorrectly called electricity pylons) carry high-voltage power lines. Sometimes, they follow the line of a motorway.
I-Spy for 5

Where work, such as surveying, must be done, vehicles towing triangular warning signs can be used. This kind of work is always on the move so that the warning sign must be easily moved.
I-Spy for 20

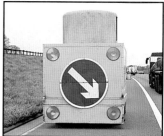

...and further on another mobile sign instructs traffic to keep right.
I-Spy for 20

Motorways sometimes have to pass over and under other kinds of transport routes. Various kinds of bridges are used for the task. Here is a selection:

Typical road bridge over a motorway.
I-Spy for **5**

Motorway crossing a very wide river on a suspension bridge.
I-Spy for **20**

Footbridge over a motorway.
I-Spy for **10**

Motorway viaduct.
I-Spy for **15**

| Railway bridge over a motorway. *I-Spy for 15* | Motorway viaduct over a canal. *I-Spy for 20* | *I-Spy 10 each for two more kinds of bridges* |

On a long motorway journey, it is important that the driver should make regular stops and perhaps take a non-alcoholic drink and a light meal, or just have a rest. Service areas are spaced at regular intervals along most motorways. Or, of course, the vehicle may need to be refuelled. A sign like this indicates how far away the next two service areas are.

I-Spy for 5

At a distance of ¹/₂ mile from the service area exit, you will see a sign like this one. It may give the name of the service area, the company that operates it, and the facilities available, such as petrol, drinks, disabled facilities, and an information centre.

I-Spy for 5

This indicates the exit road from the motorway into the service area.

I-Spy for 5

And just as you reach the service area, the regulations which apply on the motor-way come to an end.
I-Spy for **5**

On some motorways, the service area is clearly visible from the driving lanes, and there may be a covered pedestrian bridge across the motorway to another part of the service area.
I-Spy for **15**

Within the service area, you'll Spy more signs directing different kinds of traffic to the various parking areas and to the fuel pumps. The lanes indicated by the red disc with the horizontal band are no-entry lanes for vehicles.
I-Spy for 5

As well as the car and lorry parking areas, this sign also indicates caravan parking and the motel. Which two words have been mixed to make the word 'motel'?

I-Spy for 15
Double with answer

Some service areas have tables and chairs arranged in a pleasant outside area so that drivers and their passengers can enjoy the fresh air in clement weather.
I-Spy for **15**

And inside, you'll usually find a restaurant or snack bar.
I-Spy for **5**

You may want a magazine, a book, some sweets, or something else for the journey. Many motorway services have a convenient shop.
I-Spy for **5**

But if you want a longer break and a complete change from driving, there are often various kinds of coin-operated amusements.
I-Spy for **5**

Some cars are fitted with telephones these days but all motorway service areas have public telephones. Here there are 'Card phones' as well as the usual coin-operated telephones.
I-Spy for 5

Right up to date, here are British Telecom phone boxes decked out in their 1991 livery and colours.
I-Spy for 5

22

Some motorway service area have an Automobile Association information booth where you can also become a member of the AA.
I-Spy for 10

And here's a good way of asking people not to drop their litter on the motorway. In fact, throwing drinks cans or bottles out of a moving car window can be very dangerous.
I-Spy for 15

EVERY DAY THIS MUCH LITTER LANDS ON OUR MOTORWAYS.

MOTORWAY LITTER. LET'S DRIVE THE PROBLEM HOME.

Check your weight? You might find one of these coin-operated weighing machines in a service area.
I-Spy for 10

Back on the road, this sign tells you that there is an area ahead where there are outside tables and seats so that you can have your own picnic.
I-Spy for 15

Direction signs which are painted brown, such as this one, usually indicate some kind of tourist facility or attraction. In which famous seaside resort is the 'Golden Mile'.

I-Spy for 10
Double with answer

Among the most interesting things to look out for on the motorway are the different kinds of vehicles — some of them are most unusual and you will not often see them on ordinary roads. Here is a selection:

Military vehicles
*I-Spy for **15***

Large motor caravan
*I-Spy for **15***

Small motor caravan. This one is quite old fashioned. *I-Spy for **15***

Non-hazardous
liquid bulk
transporter
I-Spy for 15

Articulated lorry
What does 'articu-
lated' mean when
applied to a large
lorry?

I-Spy for 5
Double with answer

Articulated lorry
This one is transporting cylinders of compressed air.
I-Spy for 20

Score 20 for each of 2 other kinds of unusual loads.

If a vehicle is involved in a crash or if it breaks down on the motorway, it may need to be towed away.
I-Spy for 15

Have you ever wondered what the raised tarmac ramps are that you see at intervals along the sides of motorways? As you can see, these are ramps for police patrol vehicles where they can keep a watch on passing

traffic to make sure no one is speeding or breaking any other regulations.
I-Spy for **10**
Double with a police patrol vehicle on it

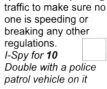

The police use various kinds of patrol vehicles on the motorway including some that are unmarked. Here is a selection. Notice that the different colours and badges indicate the different regional forces:

Jaguar XJ6
This is capable of 140 mph (225 km/h)
I-Spy for **15**

Vauxhall Senator
This is also a 140-mph (225-km/h) vehicle
I-Spy for **15**

I-Spy **10** *each for 2 other makes of fast patrol car*

Range Rover
The big, powerful, four-wheel drive Range Rover is a very versatile police patrol vehicle and can even be used to remove crashed vehicles from the motorway in an emergency.
I-Spy for 15

The Land Rover Discovery is more economical than the Range Rover but it is less powerful and rather more like the Japanese off-road vehicles.
I-Spy for 15

This police Discovery is equipped with a telescopic arm with rotatable flood lights at the top. These can be used to illuminate the scene of an accident, for example.
I-Spy for 25

THE POLICE

High-intensity, flashing red lights show that a police vehicle is stationary.
I-Spy for **15**

A motorway police patrol officer has stopped a lorry.
I-Spy for **15**

The police use helicopters mainly for crime work, for which they have a 100 per cent success rate, but some forces also use them to notify patrol cars on the ground about vehicles exceeding the speed limit, for example.
I-Spy for **20**

One of the more routine tasks carried out by motorway police patrol vehicles is escorting abnormal loads, which may be very wide...

I-Spy for **20**

...or very long
I-Spy for **20**

Bits of tyres on the hard shoulder are a surprisingly common sight on motorways. The police are responsible for clearing them from the motorway lanes but then the local authority must take the debris away.
I-Spy for 10

The tyre debris comes from tyres that have shredded. This is more common on lorries where the tyre is punctured and the weight of the lorry driven at speed causes the tyre to shred. On double wheels, the driver may not even notice the blow out immediately.
I-Spy for 15

When the time comes to leave the motor-way, the driver must look out for the correct junction. The junction number is given on a black background and these numbers are shown on road atlases.
I-Spy for **5**

Sometimes, there is a hazard on the exit lane and the traffic must be diverted.
I-Spy for **15**

'Count-down' markers indicate the approaching exit at...

300 yards distant...
I-Spy for **5**

200 yards...
I-Spy for **5**

100 yards...
I-Spy for **5**

And here is a complicated slip road from a motorway.
I-Spy for 15

As you reach the end of the slip road leaving the motorway, look out for the 'End of motorway' sign. Where there is a hard shoulder on the slip road, it is placed just at the end of it.
I-Spy for 5

35

Some vehicles, especially tankers, which may be carrying dangerous goods, must display hazard information panels. Such harmful materials include inflammable liquids or gases, poisonous or radioactive materials. One reason for this is that, if there is an accident causing spillage of the goods, the emergency services will know how to deal with it. Here are the seven panels which are used in the Transport Hazard Information System.

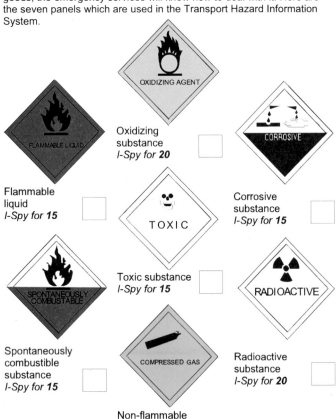

Oxidizing substance
I-Spy for 20

Flammable liquid
I-Spy for 15

Corrosive substance
I-Spy for 15

Toxic substance
I-Spy for 15

Spontaneously combustible substance
I-Spy for 15

Radioactive substance
I-Spy for 20

Non-flammable compressed gas
I-Spy for 15

How about having some fun on a car journey by playing car number games? But, whatever you do, don't distract the driver — he or she must concentrate on driving. You could even try making up your own games but here are some to start you off:

Words on a plate

Sometimes — quite often, in fact — the index letters on a car registration plate make up complete words. For example, a Portsmouth index ending in OW could make BOW, COW, HOW, LOW, MOW, NOW, ROW, SOW, TOW, VOW, and so on. Keep your eyes open as you travel, and make a list of, say, the first ten proper words you can Spy. Then try to make up the longest sentence you can out of those words.

Time traveller

As you know, the letter which prefixes a modern number plate or which, between 1963 and 1983, came after the numbers on the registration index indicates the year in which the car was registered. Try taking a journey in time by Spying, in the first place, a car with the current year's registration letter. That's obviously very easy because there are thousands of cars on the road with this year's letter. Then look for last year's letter, then the one before that, and so on in order back in time. You'll find that it gets harder and harder the further back you go. See who can go back the furthest before you get to the end of your trip.

Easy phrase or saying

Just take the letters of the first car registration plate you see to be the initial letters of words, and then try to make up a short phrase or saying from the words. For example, if you saw a car from Glasgow with the registration letters EGB, you could say 'Eat Good Bread'.

Rising numbers

This is a simple one: just find a car number ending in 1, then look for 2, and so on, and see how high you can get. You could make this game more difficult by looking for car numbers 111, 222, 333, and so on.

That's my number

Everyone chooses a number, which they announce to the others in the car. Each person then has to Spy a car on which the numbers of the registration plate add up to the number announced. The winner is the first person to Spy the car. For example, if someone announces '22', then a car number 688 would be correct — 6 + 8 + 8 = 22.

Pub Cricket

This is a popular game for a car journey although, as you will realize, you don't see many pubs beside motorways. On the other hand, pubs are often seen in the vicinity of motorway junctions so you can still play the game when you are approaching or leaving the motorway.

So, look out for any pub or inn signs that you pass. You score one point for each leg, human or animal, in the name of an inn. For example, the Hare and Hounds would score 8, the Horse and Jockey 6, and so on. Any inn name connected with royalty scores an extra point so that The King George IV scores 3. Any sign connected with Arms, such as the Bricklayer's Arms or Carpenter's Arms, loses you 2 points.

Finally, because a fish has neither arms nor legs, a fish on an inn sign, such as The Perch or The Trout, bowls you out and you lose all your score and start again. You can take turns batting or bowling.

| Team 1 |
| Captain _____ |

| Team 2 |
| Captain _____ |

Car Census

To pass the time on a motorway, you could carry out your own 'straw poll' on the popularity of makes of cars. We have made a list of car manufacturers and put them into a grid. Every time you see one of these makes of cars, just put a tick in the grid. (This list has been drawn up using *I-Spy Cars* as a guide.)

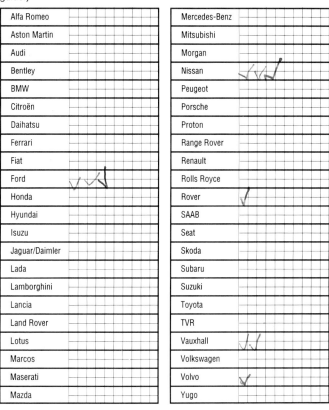

			Mercedes-Benz		
Alfa Romeo			Mercedes-Benz		
Aston Martin			Mitsubishi		
Audi			Morgan		
Bentley			Nissan	✓✓✓	
BMW			Peugeot		
Citroën			Porsche		
Daihatsu			Proton		
Ferrari			Range Rover		
Fiat			Renault		
Ford	✓✓✓		Rolls Royce		
Honda			Rover	✓	
Hyundai			SAAB		
Isuzu			Seat		
Jaguar/Daimler			Skoda		
Lada			Subaru		
Lamborghini			Suzuki		
Lancia			Toyota		
Land Rover			TVR		
Lotus			Vauxhall	✓✓	
Marcos			Volkswagen		
Maserati			Volvo	✓	
Mazda			Yugo		

You could also make up your own grid and tick off any other makes of cars that you Spy.

·CAR NUMBERS·

In England, Scotland, and Wales today, car numbers, or registration index marks as they are more properly called, are usually made up of up to seven characters. These are often a letter of the alphabet, followed by three numbers from 1 to 999, and then between one and three more letters of the alphabet. This system has not always been quite the same.

From 1904 to 1974, car numbers were issued by County Councils and County Borough Councils but, since 1 October 1974, they have been issued by the Department of Transport's Vehicle Registration Offices. Originally, the first car number issued might have been A 1; then A 2, A 3, and so on up to A 9999. After that, there could be AA 1 to AA 9999 until these combinations ran out when AB 1 to AB 9999 would be possible. Then, after the two-letter marks ran out, three letter marks were introduced. Eventually, all possible combinations were exhausted so the numbers were put before the letters but no registration mark could be longer than six characters.

Nowadays, some of these early number plates are highly prized and change hands for quite large sums of money. And there are also other unusual number plates which convey some special meaning, such as the name of the owner. There is a selection throughout the list.

In 1963, some of the Councils around the country where cars were more common, ran out of all possible combinations of three letter marks and numbers. This meant that another system had to be worked out and, in 1965, the new system was adopted throughout the country.

Each year from 1965, the combination of three letters and up to three numbers from 1 to 999 was followed by a letter to indicate the year. Some letters, such as I, O, Q, U, and Z, have not been used. Finally, on 1 August 1983, the year letter was placed before the numbers 1 to 999 followed by the three letter combination. On the 1 August 1990, new cars were given registration marks prefixed by the letter H.

The second two letters of three letter combinations which are issued currently indicate the various Vehicle Registration Offices and Councils to which the numbers have been issued. For example, all registration marks in which the second two letters are AA, such as AAA to HAA, JAA to PAA, and RAA to YAA, have been issued by the Vehicle Registration Office at Bournemouth.

The lists below give all of the index mark suffixes available for England, Scotland, and Wales with the Vehicle Registration Office that issues them. The first list is arranged in order of the suffix letters while the second list is in order of the issuing offices. In the first list, put a tick in the box alongside a suffix the first time you see a number which includes it. When you have collected 250 numbers, add 100 to your I-Spy total.

☐ AA	Bournemouth	☐ BS	Aberdeen	☐ CY	Swansea
☑ AB	Worcester	☐ BT	Leeds		
☐ AC	Coventry	☐ BU	Manchester	☐ DA	Birmingham
☐ AD	Gloucester	☐ BV	Preston	☐ DB	Manchester
☐ AE	Bristol	☐ BW	Oxford	☐ DC	Middlesborough
☐ AF	Truro	☐ BX	Haverfordwest	☐ DD	Gloucester
☐ AG	Hull	☐ BY	London NW	☐ DE	Haverfordwest
☐ AH	Norwich			☑ DF	Gloucester
☐ AJ	Middlesborough	☐ CA	Chester	☐ DG	Gloucester
☐ AK	Sheffield	☐ CB	Manchester	☐ DH	Dudley
☐ AL	Nottingham	☐ CC	Bangor	☐ DJ	Liverpool
☐ AM	Swindon	☐ CD	Brighton	☐ DK	Manchester
☐ AN	Reading	☐ CE	Peterborough	☐ DL	Portsmouth
☐ AO	Carlisle	☐ CF	Reading	☑ DM	Chester
☐ AP	Brighton	☑ CG	Bournemouth	☐ DN	Leeds
☐ AR	Chelmsford	☑ CH	Nottingham	☐ DO	Lincoln
☑ AS	Inverness	☐ CJ	Gloucester	☐ DP	Reading
☐ AT	Hull	☐ CK	Preston	☐ DR	Exeter
☐ AU	Nottingham	☐ CL	Norwich	☐ DS	Glasgow
☐ AV	Peterborough	☐ CM	Liverpol	☐ DT	Sheffield
☑ AW	Shrewsbury	☐ CN	Newcastle upon Tyne	☐ DU	Coventry
☐ AX	Cardiff			☐ DV	Exeter
☐ AY	Leicester	☐ CO	Exeter	☑ DW	Cardiff
		☑ CP	Huddersfield	☐ DX	Ipswich
☐ BA	Manchester	☑ CR	Portsmouth	☐ DY	Brighton
☐ BB	Newcastle upon Tyne	☐ CS	Glasgow		
		☐ CT	Lincoln	☐ EA	Dudley
☐ BC	Leicester	☑ CU	Newcastle upon Tyne	☐ EB	Peterborough
☐ BD	Northampton			☑ EC	Preston
☐ BE	Lincoln	☐ CV	Truro	☐ ED	Liverpool
☐ BF	Stoke on Trent	☐ CW	Preston	☐ EF	Middlesborough
☐ BG	Liverpool	☐ CX	Huddersfield	☑ EG	Peterborough
☐ BH	Luton				
☑ BJ	Ipswich				
☑ BK	Portsmouth				
☐ BL	Reading				
☑ BM	Luton				
☐ BN	Manchester				
☐ BO	Cardiff				
☐ BP	Portsmouth				
☐ BR	Newcastle upon Tyne				

CAR NUMBERS

EH	Stoke on Trent	✓ GA	Glasgow	HT	Bristol
EJ	Haverfordwest	✓ GB	Glasgow	HU	Bristol
EK	Liverpool	GC	London SW	HV	London C
✓ EL	Bournemouth	GD	Glasgow	HW	Bristol
EM	Liverpool	GE	Glasgow	HX	London C
EN	Manchester	GF	London SW	HY	Bristol
EO	Preston	✓ GG	Glasgow		
EP	Swansea	GH	London SW	JA	Manchester
ER	Peterborough	GJ	London SW	JB	Reading
ES	Dundee	GK	London SW	✓ JC	Bangor
ET	Sheffield	GL	Truro	JD	London C
EU	Bristol	GM	Reading	JE	Peterborough
EV	Chelmsford	GN	London SW	JF	Leicester
EW	Peterborough	GO	London SW	JG	Maidstone
EX	Norwich	GP	London SW	✓ JH	Reading
✓ EY	Bangor	GR	Newcastle upon Tyne	JJ	Maidstone
				JK	Brighton
FA	Stoke on Trent	GS	Luton	JL	Lincoln
FB	Bristol	GT	London SW	JM	Reading
FC	Oxford	GU	London SE	JN	Chelmsford
FD	Dudley	✓ GV	Ipswich	JO	Oxford
FE	Lincoln	GW	London SE	✓ JP	Liverpool
FF	Bangor	GX	London SE	JR	Newcastle upon Tyne
FG	Brighton	GY	London SE		
FH	Gloucester			✓ JS	Inverness
FJ	Exeter	HA	Dudley	JT	Bournemouth
FK	Dudley	HB	Cardiff	JU	Leicester
FL	Peterborough	HC	Brighton	JV	Lincoln
FM	Chester	HD	Huddersfield	JW	Birmingham
FN	Maidstone	HE	Sheffield	JX	Huddersfield
FO	Gloucester	HF	Liverpool	JY	Exeter
FP	Leicester	HG	Preston		
FR	Preston	✓ HH	Carlisle	KA	Liverpool
✓ FS	Edinburgh	HJ	Chelmsford	KB	Liverpool
✓ FT	Newcastle upon Tyne	HK	Chelmsford	KC	Liverpool
		HL	Sheffield	✓ KD	Liverpool
FU	Lincoln	✓ HM	London C	✓ KE	Maidstone
FV	Preston	✓ HN	Middlesborough	KF	Liverpool
FW	Lincoln	HO	Bournemouth	✓ KG	Cardiff
FX	Bournemouth	✓ HP	Coventry	KH	Hull
FY	Liverpool	HR	Swindon	KJ	Maidstone
		✓ HS	Glasgow	KK	Maidstone

KL	Maidstone	LV	Liverpool	NE	Manchester
KM	Maidstone	LW	London NW	NF	Manchester
KN	Maidstone	LX	London NW	NG	Norwich
KO	Maidstone	LY	London NW	NH	Northampton
KP	Maidstone			NJ	Brighton
KR	Maidstone	MA	Chester	NK	Luton
KS	Edinburgh	MB	Chester	NL	Newcastle upon Tyne
KT	Maidstone	MC	London NE		
KU	Sheffield	MD	London NE	NM	Luton
KV	Coventry	ME	London NE	NN	Nottingham
KW	Sheffield	MF	London NE	NO	Chelmsford
KX	Luton	MG	London NE	NP	Worcester
KY	Sheffield	MH	London NE	NR	Leicester
		MJ	Luton	NS	Glasgow
LA	London NW	MK	London NE	NT	Shrewsbury
LB	London NW	ML	London NE	NU	Nottingham
LC	London NW	MM	London NE	NV	Northampton
LD	London NW	MN	not used	NW	Leeds
LE	London NW	MO	Reading	NX	Dudley
LF	London NW	MP	London NE	NY	Cardiff
LG	Chester	MR	Swindon		
LH	London NW	MS	Edinburgh	OA	Birmingham
LJ	Bournemouth	MT	London NE	OB	Birmingham
LK	London NW	MU	London NE	OC	Birmingham
LL	London NW	MV	London NE	OD	Exeter
LM	London NW	MW	Swindon	OE	Birmingham
LN	London NW	MX	London NE	OF	Birmingham
LO	London NW	MY	London NE	OG	Birmingham
LP	London NW			OH	Birmingham
LR	London NW	NA	Manchester	OJ	Birmingham
LS	Edinburgh	NB	Manchester	OK	Birmingham
LT	London NW	NC	Manchester	OL	Birmingham
LU	London NW	ND	Manchester	OM	Birmingham

43

CAR NUMBERS

☐	ON	Birmingham				
☑	OO	Chelmsford				
☑	OP	Birmingham				
☐	OR	Portsmouth				
☐	OS	Glasgow				
☐	OT	Portsmouth				
☐	OU	Bristol				
☐	OV	Birmingham				
☐	OW	Portsmouth				
☐	OX	Birmingham				
☐	OY	London NW				

☑	PA	Guildford	☐	RF	Stoke on Trent	☑	SL	Dundee
☑	PN	Guildford	☑	RG	Newcastle upon	☐	SM	Carlisle
☑	PC	Guildford			Tyne	☑	SN	Dundee
☐	PD	Guildford	☐	RH	Hull	☑	SO	Aberdeen
☐	PE	Guildford	☐	RJ	Manchester	☐	SP	Dundee
☐	PF	Guildford	☐	RK	London NW	☐	SR	Dundee
☐	PG	Guildford	☐	RL	Truro	☑	SS	Aberdeen
☐	PH	Guildford	☑	RM	Carlisle	☑	ST	Inverness
☐	PJ	Guildford	☐	RN	Preston	☐	SU	Glasgow
☐	PK	Guildford	☐	RO	Luton	☐	SV	unused
☐	PL	Guildford	☐	RP	Northampton	☐	SW	Carlisle
☐	PM	Guildford	☐	RR	Nottingham	☐	SX	Edinburgh
☐	PN	Guildford	☐	RS	Aberdeen	☐	SY	unused
☐	PO	Portsmouth	☐	RT	Ipswich			
☐	PP	Luton	☐	RU	Bournemouth	☐	TA	Exeter
☐	PR	Bournemouth	☐	RV	Portsmouth	☐	TB	Liverpool
☑	PS	Aberdeen	☐	RW	Coventry	☑	TC	Bristol
☑	PT	Newcastle upon	☐	RX	Reading	☐	TD	Manchester
		Tyne	☐	RY	Leicester	☐	TE	Manchester
☐	PU	Chelmsford				☐	TF	Reading
☐	PV	Ipswich	☑	SA	Aberdeen	☐	TG	Cardiff
☐	PW	Norwich	☐	SB	Glasgow	☐	TH	Swansea
☐	PX	Portsmouth	☑	SC	Edinburgh	☐	TJ	Liverpool
☐	PY	Middlesborough	☐	SD	Glasgow	☐	TK	Exeter
			☐	SE	Aberdeen	☐	TL	Lincoln
☐	RA	Nottingham	☑	SF	Edinburgh	☑	TM	Luton
☐	RB	Nottingham	☑	SG	Edinburgh	☐	TN	Newcastle upon
☐	RC	Nottingham	☐	SH	Edinburgh			Tyne
☐	RD	Reading	☑	SJ	Glasgow	☐	TO	Nottingham
☑	RE	Stoke on Trent	☐	SK	Inverness	☑	TP	Portsmouth

TR	Portsmouth	VG	Norwich			
TS	Dundee	VH	Huddersfield			
TT	Exeter	VJ	Gloucester			
TU	Chester	VK	Newcastle upon			
TV	Nottingham		Tyne			
TW	Chelmsford	VL	Lincoln			
TX	Cardiff	VM	Manchester			
✓ TY	Newcastle upon	VN	Middlesborough			
	Tyne	VO	Nottingham			
		✓ VP	Birmingham			
UA	Leeds	✓ VR	Manchester			
UB	Leeds	VS	Luton			
UC	London C	✓ VT	Stoke on Trent			
✓ UD	Oxford	VU	Manchester			
✓ UE	Dudley	VV	Northampton			
UF	Brighton	VW	Chelmsford			
UG	Leeds	VX	Chelmsford			
UH	Cardiff	VY	Leeds			
UJ	Shrewsbury					
UK	Birmingham	WA	Sheffield			
UL	London C	WB	Sheffield			
UM	Leeds	WC	Chelmsford			
UN	Exeter	WD	Dudley			
UO	Exeter	WE	Sheffield			
UP	Newcastle upon	WF	Sheffield			
	Tyne	WG	Sheffield			
UR	Luton	WH	Manchester			
✓ US	Glasgow	WJ	Sheffield			
UT	Leicester	WK	Coventry			
UU	London C	WL	Oxford			
UV	London C	WM	Liverpool			
✓ UW	London C	WN	Swansea			
UX	Shrewsbury	WO	Cardiff			
UY	Worcester	WP	Worcester			
		WR	Leeds			
VA	Peterborough	WS	Bristol			
VB	Maidstone	WT	Leeds			
✓ VC	Coventry	WU	Leeds			
VD	series with-	✓ WV	Brighton			
	drawn	WW	Leeds			
VE	Peterborough	WX	Leeds			
VF	Norwich	WY	Leeds			

At the moment, all the X suffixes are spare.

✓ YA	Taunton	
YB	Taunton	
YC	Taunton	
YD	Taunton	
YE	London C	
✓ YF	London C	
YG	Leeds	
YH	London C	
YJ	Brighton	
YK	London C	
✓ YL	London C	
✓ YM	London C	
YN	London C	
✓ YO	London C	
YP	London C	
✓ YR	London C	
✓ YS	Glasgow	
YT	London C	
YU	London C	
YV	London C	
YW	London C	
YX	London C	
YY	London C	

Aberdeen
BS, PS, RS, SA, SE, SO, SS

Bangor
CC, EY, FF, JC

Birmingham
DA, JW, OA, OB, OC, OE, OF, OG, OH, OJ, OK, OL, OM, ON, OP, OV, OX, UK, VP

Bournemouth
AA, CG, EL, FX, HO, JT, LJ, PR, RU

Brighton
AP, CD, DY, FG, HC, JK, NJ, UF, WV, YJ

Bristol
AE, EU, FB, HT, HU, HW, HY, OU, TC, WS

Cardiff
AX, BO, DW, HB, KG, NY, TG, TX, UH, WO

Carlisle
AO, HH, RM, SM, SW

Chelmsford
AR, EV, HJ, HK, JN, NO, OO, PU, TW, VW, VX, WC

Chester
CA, DM, FM, LG, MA, MB, TU

Coventry
AC, DU, HP, KV, RW, VC, WK

Dudley
DH, EA, FD, FK, HA, NX, UE, WD

Dundee
ES, SL, SN, SP, SR, TS

Edinburgh
FS, KS, LS, MS, SC, SF, SG, SH, SX

Exeter
CO, DR, DV, FJ, JY, OD, TA, TK, TT, UN, UO

Glasgow
CS, DS, GA, GB, GD, GE, GG, HS, NS, OS, SB, SD, SJ, SU, US, YS

Gloucester
AD, CJ, DD, DF, DG, FH, FO, VJ

Guildford
PA, PC, PD, PE, PF, PG, PH, PJ, PK, PL, PM, PN, PN

Haverfordwest
BX, DE, EJ

Huddersfield
CP, CX, HD, JX, VH

Hull
AG, AT, KH, RH

Inverness
AS, JS, SK, ST

Ipswich
BJ, DX, GV, PV, RT

Leeds
BT, DN, NW, UA, UB, UG, UM, VY, WR, WT, WU, WW, WX, WY, YG

Leicester
AY, BC, FP, JF, JU, NR, RY, UT

Lincoln
BE, CT, DO, FE, FU, FW, JL, JV, TL, VL

Liverpool
BG, CM, DJ, ED, EK, EM, FY, HF, JP, KA, KB, KC, KD, KF, LV, TB, TJ, WM

London Central
HM, HV, HX, JD, UC, UL, UU, UV, UW, YE, YF, YH, YK, YL, YM, YN, YO, YP, YR, YT, YU, YV, YW, YX, YY

London North East
MC, MD, ME, MF, MG, MH, MK, ML, MM, MP, MT, MU, MV, MX, MY

London North West
BY, LA, LB, LC, LD, LE, LF, LH, LK, LL, LM, LN, LO, LP, LR, LT, LU, LW, LX, LY, OY, RK

London South East
GU, GW, GX, GY

London South West
GC, GF, GH, GJ, GK, GN, GO, GP, GT

Luton
BH, BM, GS, KX, MJ, NK, NM, PP, RO, TM, UR, VS

Maidstone
FN, JG, JJ, KE, KJ, KK, KL, KM, KN, KO, KP, KR, KT, VB

Manchester
BA, BN, BU, CB, DB, DK, EN, JA, NA, NB, NC, ND, NE, NF, RJ, TD, TE, VM, VR, VU, WH

Middlesborough
AJ, DC, EF, HN, VN, PY

Newcastle upon Tyne
BB, BR, CN, CU, FT, GR, JR, NL, PT, RG, TN, TY, UP, VK

Northampton
BD, NH, NV, RP, VV

Norwich
AH, CL, EX, NG, PW, VF, VG

Nottingham
AL, AU, CH, NN, NU, RA, RB, RC, RR, TO, TV, VO

Oxford
BW, FC, JO, UD, WL

Peterborough
AV, CE, EB, EG, ER, EW, FL, JE, VA, VE

Portsmouth
BK, BP, CR, DL, OR, OT, OW, PO, PX, RV, TP, TR

Preston
BV, CK, CW, EC, EO, FR, FV, HG, RN

Reading
AN, BL, CF, DP, GM, JB, JH, JM, MO, RD, RX, TF

Sheffield
AK, DT, ET, HE, HL, KU, KW, KY, WA, WB, WE, WF, WG, WJ

Shrewsbury
AW, NT, UJ, UX

Stoke on Trent
BF, EH, FA, RE, RF, VT

Swansea
CY, EP, TH, WN

Swindon
AM, HR, MR, MW

Taunton
YA, YB, YC, YD

Truro
AF, CV, GL, RL

Worcester
AB, NP, UY, WP

European registration letters
The first time you see one of these plates, tick it off. When you have collected the whole set, add 50 to your I-Spy total.

	A	Austria		**H**	Hungary
	AL	Albania		**I**	Italy
	AND	Andorra		**IRL**	Ireland
	B	Belgium		**IS**	Iceland
	BG	Bulgaria		**L**	Luxembourg
	CH	Switzerland		**M**	Malta
	CS	Czechoslovakia		**MC**	Monaco
✓	**D**	Federal Republic of Germany		**N**	Norway
	DK	Denmark		**NL**	Netherlands
	E	Spain		**P**	Portugal
✓	**F**	France		**PL**	Poland
	FL	Liechtenstein		**R**	Rumania
✓	**GB**	Great Britain		**RSM**	San Marino
	GBA	Alderney		**S**	Sweden
	GBG	Guernsey ⎤ Channel Islands		**SF**	Finland
	GBJ	Jersey ⎦		**SU**	Russia
	GBM	Isle of Man		**TR**	Turkey
	GBZ	Gibraltar		**V**	Vatican City
	GR	Greece		**YU**	Yugoslavia

INDEX

© I-Spy Limited 1991

ISBN (paperback) 1 85671 055 6
ISBN (hard cover) 1 85671 056 4

Michelin Tyre Public Limited Company
Davy House, Lyon Road, Harrow, Middlesex HA1 2DQ

MICHELIN and the Michelin Man are Registered Trademarks of Michelin Tyre plc

Edited and designed by Curtis Garratt Limited, The Old Vicarage, Horton cum Studley, Oxford OX9 1BT

The Publisher gratefully acknowledges the contribution of Richard Garratt who provided the majority of the photographs in this I-Spy book. Additional photograph by the Cheshire Constabulary. The Publisher also wishes to thank Chief Inspector Barnes and Constable Ridgeway of the Cheshire Constabulary Motorway Unit and Inspector Wheeler of Thames Valley Police for their kind co-operation and assistance during the photography.

Colour reproduction by Norwich Litho Services Limited.

Printed in Spain.